EX LIBRIS

HERITAGE OF ENGLAND

Silver Through Ten Reigns

Asprey

HERITAGE

OF

ENGLAND

SILVER THROUGH TEN REIGNS

PATRON
HIS GRACE THE DUKE OF GRAFTON K.G.

IN AID OF THE

ROYAL OAK FOUNDATION

Written and Researched by JAMES CHARLES

ASPREY & COMPANY
165–169 New Bond Street, W1.

1983

HER MAJESTY QUEEN ELIZABETH
THE QUEEN MOTHER

President of the National Trust

BRITAIN salutes New York is the very first international arts festival to be held in the city. The purpose is to commemorate the bicentenary of the 1783 Peace Treaty between Great Britain and the United States. The festival covers many social and cultural events, including major art exhibitions and performing arts programmes. These are taking place at The Lincoln Center, Carnegie Hall, The Metropolitan Museum of Art, The Museum of Modern Art and The Cooper-Hewitt Museum among others.

To present a balanced cross-section of British culture, exhibitions that are being held include a collection of paintings and miniatures by Hans Holbein from Windsor Castle, paintings by John Constable, works by Henry Moore and a fine collection of paintings from The Royal Academy showing 200 years of British art. There is also an exhibition showing England's role in the history of glass.

Asprey's contribution to the festival is to host this exhibition of English antique silver.

Britain Salutes New York 1983.
New York International Arts Festival.

THE VISCOUNT NORWICH. Honorary Trustee of The Royal Oak Foundation, Inc.

ASPREY and the National Trust are great British institutions and it is exciting that they are now both represented in New York. The National Trust formed its American affiliate, The Royal Oak Foundation, in 1973, as a non-profit making corporation.

Ten years later, as Britain Salutes New York, it is particularly fitting that Asprey and the Royal Oak have come together to present this exhibition. Asprey has a long-standing reputation for quality while the National Trust is probably the world's richest storehouse of fine architecture and works of art. From the collections of the Trust Asprey has selected treasures for its 'Heritage of England' exhibition from Ickworth in East Anglia and Dunham Massey in the North – two of the Trust's 150 country houses and castles which Royal Oak members support and may visit free of charge.

The Royal Oak Foundation is grateful for the generosity of Asprey in donating the profits of the souvenir catalogue.

All of us who value the links that bind our two great countries together, look forward to the bonds being strengthened through Asprey and Company and the Royal Oak Foundation.

THE VISCOUNT NORWICH.

ASPREY are extremely proud to have the opportunity to present this exhibition of English Silver. Many of the objects shown here have never before left the shores of England.

We wish to thank Her Majesty Queen Elizabeth II for her gracious loan of the gold medallion by Simon de Passe of Elizabeth I. The Victoria & Albert Museum, The Worshipful Company of Goldsmiths, The National Trust, Tudor House Museum–Southampton, Hampshire County Museum Service and the private collectors, who have by their generosity made it possible for us to show you these superb objects in the heart of New York.

It is impossible to thank everyone individually here but we would like to offer our especial thanks to Philippa Glanville of the Victoria and Albert Museum, Rosemary Ransome-Wallis of the Goldsmiths Hall and Claude Blair lately keeper of the Department of Metalwork at the Victoria and Albert Museum and Shirley Bury, present keeper, for their help and encouragement in the preparation of this exhibition.

J.R. Asprey

J.R. ASPREY, APRIL 1983

'MARVEL NOT at the gold and the expense but at the craftsmanship of the work.'

SO WROTE the great twelfth-century art-patron, Abbot Suger about his work at the Abbey of St. Denis near Paris, but his words have a general application to all works of art, and are as valid now as they ever were. They of course apply particularly to works of art made from precious metals which, because they are precious, have always been used as much for the display and storage of wealth as for making things that were to be beautiful for their own sakes.

Until comparatively recently gold, silver plate, and jewellery were ruthlessly melted down when their owners were in need of cash, or thought that something more up-to-date was needed, and, in consequence, only a minute number of the pieces made in earlier centuries have survived. With the 19th century, and its improved living standards and more widespread education, the attitude advocated by Suger came to be generally accepted as the proper one, even though the more elaborate works of Victorian craftsmanship in silver usually contained a substantial amount – even an excess – of bullion! This changed attitude, which was accompanied by a tremendous interest in the development of historic styles, led to an appreciation, amongst other things, of early works of art in metal, including gold and silver. Because these had become valued for their craftsmanship or historical associations, this led to the preservation of much that earlier generations would have destroyed. The publication in 1863 of Chaffer's 'Hallmarks of Gold and Silver Plate' would hardly have been possible at a much earlier period, and it can be regarded as the starting-point for the study of British silver, though it was not until the beginning of the present century that its qualities began to be generally appreciated.

Those qualities – and especially the elegance and panache of the products of the great 18th century silversmiths – need no introduction to the American public; they have known and appreciated them almost as long as they have been appreciated in their country of origin. The main purpose of the present exhibition is to display them once more, but in a group of loan objects that will not be familiar to most Americans since they have never been exhibited in the United States before. It gives me great pleasure to introduce them to what I hope will be a large number of visitors.

CLAUDE BLAIR, FORMERLY KEEPER OF THE DEPARTMENT OF METALWORK, VICTORIA AND ALBERT MUSEUM.

CONTENTS

CONTENTS

THE Campion Cup, a silver gilt font shaped cup, now without a cover, with an inscription in lombardic letters. The words divided by pomegranates engraved around the bowl on a matted ground 'SOLI DEO HONOR ET GLORIA.' 'Honour and Glory Belong to God Alone.'

*London, 1500/1
Maker's mark,
a covered cup
Height, 3⅛ inches*

FORMERLY in the possession of the Campions of Danny, Hurstpierpoint, Sussex. This, the earliest known example of a marked font cup, demonstrates the form of the most popular early Tudor drinking cup or 'bowl'. The shape remained popular until about 1575; the Cressner Cup of 1503 at the Goldsmiths Company retains its cover but others such as the Bodkin Cup in the Portsmouth civic plate, and another in the Norwich civic plate, have lost theirs. The inscription indicates that this bowl was intended for ceremonial communal drink that was taken at the saying of grace before meat; the Howard Grace Cup is an example of the same custom. The great rarity of early English plate, with perhaps only three hundred pieces surviving from before the mid-16th century, makes generalization unwise but it seems that an appropriate inscription was more common than not. Some were dedicatory, where a piece was given for use in a Church or Chantry Chapel, others record the presentation of plate to brotherhood in fellowship, as in the case of livery company silver.

LENT BY THE VICTORIA AND ALBERT MUSEUM.

Formerly in the collection of Sir Samuel Montagu.
Exhibited Loan Exhibition 1902, *Case J. No. 3,
Plate 36 and illustrated in the catalogue J. Starkie
Gardner F.S.A.* Old Silver Work Chiefly English
From 15th to 18th Centuries.

N. M. Penzer Tudor Font Shaped Cups *Apollo,
Part 1 Dec. 1957 pp.174–179.*
Charles Oman English Engraved Silver *p.27.*

Plate 1

A SERPENTINE marble bowl, the broad everted rim has a border of engraved leaves at the junction of the marble, the applied circular foot decorated with broad shaped ribs and bead work, the upper part has a serrated strip clasping the base of the bowl.

London, circa 1510
Unmarked
Diameter, 9¼ inches

THIS is the equivalent in stone of the popular wooden drinking vessels (Mazers), which were made from the 13th to the 16th Century; like many of the surviving mazers, it has been fitted with mounts of precious metal to enhance its appearance and, by association, raise the social standing of its owner. The English taste for drinking from vessels of natural materials–wood, stone, horn, ivory–with mounts, was to flourish until the early 17th Century. This bowl was formerly in the collection of Lord Swaythling, who lent his plate to the Victoria and Albert Museum from 1911 till his death in 1924. The collection was then sold at auction 6th May, 1924 when the museum bought this cup and other items.

LENT BY THE VICTORIA AND ALBERT MUSEUM.

Exhibited at the Burlington Fine Arts Club 1901.
Exhibited in the Loan Collection at St. James's Court, 1902 *and illustrated in the catalogue* Old Silver Work *by J. Starkie Gardner F.S.A. pl.35 Fig. 1.*
Illustrated in A History of English Plate *by Sir Charles Jackson Vol. II, p.637, Fig. 859.*

J.K.D. Cooper A re-assessment of some English Late Gothic and Early Renaissance Plate *Burlington Magazine, Volume CX 1p. 408–412 pl.39.*

Plate II

THE Deane Cup, the spreading shallow bowl of circular outline, with slightly inverted rim, the bowl engraved with four leafed stylized rosettes between each Tudor word, the following motto: 'GIVE GOD THAKES FOR ALL THYNGS' on coarse 'zig-zag' ground. The centre of the bowl, which is slightly depressed, is incised with a helmeted head in profile, placed within a border of plain double lines resembling the Lombardic I and another stamp filled by crossed lines.

THE thick, short stem is formed by a die-struck convex collar ornamented with medallions of heads and seeded roses on stalks. From this hangs a plain frill overlapping the top of the pillar, which is chased in low relief with an acanthus leaf, and surrounded at its junction with the foot by a thick corded moulding. The foot widens out as a broad band of radiating tongue like straps between which the ground is cut into deep horizontal grooves. The rim is concave in shape and ornamented by a stamped moulding of beautiful design, alternately plain tongues and lilies on stalks; the extreme edge is of rounded wire, as is usual in Tudor work. Inscription under the bowl 'Ex done Dorotheae Wither de Hall, Viduae 1698'.

London, 1551/2 by Robert Danbe Height, 5¼ inches

After the Reformation confiscation of Mass-chalices, there was no prejudice in the English church against the use of secular plate for the bread and wine at communion services. Many parishes were given pieces of old plate, no longer fashionable, when the need arose, and much historic silver has been preserved because of this, for example the pair of Elizabethan flagons from Westwell Church *(No. 8)* and the Tyssen Flagon *(No. 14)*. In this instance the date on which the cup was presented to Deane Church as a communion cup is engraved with the name of the donor, Dorothy Wither, under the foot.

While the general form of the cup and details such as the gadrooned foot are characteristic of earlier 16th Century plate, the incorporation of a warrior's head in the centre of the bowl is a device commonly used on the later more elegant Elizabethan form of drinking cup, the tazza.

The font-shaped cup had a long popularity in England. The earliest hallmarked example, the Campion Cup, is also to be seen in this Exhibition, *(No. 1.)* Both, from the inscriptions engraved on them, may be classed as grace cups with which a communal ceremonial toast was drunk after the grace had been said.

The Withers originated in Lancashire at the time of Henry I. A family member settled in Manydown near Basingstoke, Hampshire, later marrying into a local land-owning family, the Ayliffes, who *claimed*

claimed descent by marriage from William of Wykeham. The cup was apparently brought into the family by Agnes, wife of the second George, (son of Gilbert Wither); she possessed a quantity of plate among which was a 'guilt wyn bowl'. This heirloom she left to Joan, her niece, by marriage. Joan's husband, George Wither of Winchester left it to her cousin Charles who subsequently married Dorothy of the inscription.

The Deane Cup can be compared favourably with the Kremlin Cup 1557 which was probably one of the pieces of ambassadorial plate given to the Tzar; the shallow bowl is engraved on the outside of its narrow vertical sides with sprays of floral arabesques on a hatched ground, bound top and bottom by interlacing bands of vertical ribbed strapwork. Inside the bowl on a slightly convex centre is engraved with the head and shoulders of a classical warrior, the maker's mark is illegible but may possibly be R.D. in monogram, the maker of the Deane Cup. We have already noted several similarities between the two cups, but if we look closely at the floral band and ribbed strap-work round the mouth of the 1567 flagon by R.D. at the Armourers and brasiers (for one side of which see H.D. Ellis, 1892 catalogue pl. 111, No. 5, and for the other side see 1927 V & A catalogue of the Livery Companies Exhibition pl. XXVI) we shall see that it is almost identical with the engraving on the Kremlin Cup.

LENT BY HAMPSHIRE COUNTY MUSEUM SERVICE.

Formerly in the possession of the Church of All Saints, Deane, Hampshire.
Sold at Sotheby's 17th June 1971 *Lot No. 168.*
Charles Oman 1557–1663 The English Silver in the Kremlin *1961.*

Rev. P.R.P. Braithwaite Church Plate of Hampshire *London 1909, pp. 100–1.*
Country Life Church Treasures in Peril *February 7th, 1974.*
N.M. Penzer Tudor Font Shaped Cups *Apollo, November 1957, Feb/March 1958.*

Plate III

Plate IV, Helmeted head in profile.

Plate V, Hallmarks.

Plate VI, Inscription under bowl.

A CASTER, silver gilt, in the form of a covered cup on a foot surmounted by a pierced cap, the body and foot are chased and embossed with bunches of fruit in strapwork panels, the flange is cut by four rectangular notches presumably to secure a removable cresting or cover. This piece, and four salts dating between 1563 and 1587 were purchased by the museum from the Mostyn family of Mostyn Hall Flintshire in 1886.

London, 1563/4
Maker's mark,
indecipherable
Height, 4¼ inches

TUDOR references to casters for pepper as a separate item of table plate are rare. Goldsmiths soon recognised that it was more convenient to provide a receptacle for pepper or spice within the cover of the salt itself. Casting bottles for water are more commonly referred to, as for example in the inventories of the Tudor royal plate quoted in Collin's study, and several have survived, albeit considerably smaller than the elaborate heavy specimens in Henry VIII, collection. The earliest example of 1546 is in the Victoria and Albert Museum, it is stylistically close to another silver flask in the Irwin Untermyer collection.

An eleventh century crystal bottle, presumably from a reliquary broken up at the Reformation, has silver gilt mounts and a pierced cover. A further casting bottle of about 1560 is in the British Museum. The form of all these casting bottles is that of an accessory for wearing or tucking into the sleeve and fitted with a suspension chain.

The function of this caster which is clearly designed to stand on its broad base is not certain; however, the parallels between the scale and ornament and that of the other three small salts in the Mostyn Collection support the assumption that it was intended to contain a dry condiment rather than perfumed water for toilet use.

LENT BY THE VICTORIA AND ALBERT MUSEUM.

Charles Oman English Domestic Silver *p.64.*

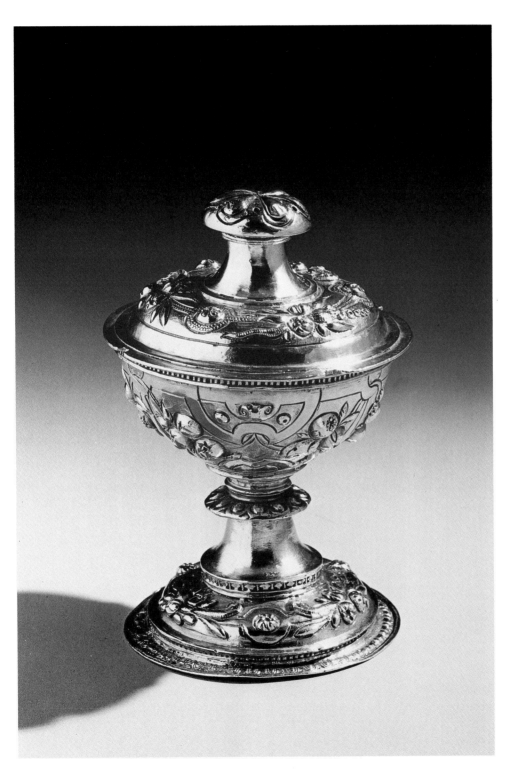

Plate VII

AN early Elizabeth I silver gilt tazza on circular spreading domed foot, repousse and chased with a band of marine creatures below a bold knopped baluster shaped stem cast with fruit clusters, the circular bowl with chased interior depicting the meeting of Isaac and Rebecca within a laurel border and below an engraved rim of arabesques and strapwork further enriched on exterior with animals and insects, the underbowl ornately repousse with fruit and foliate clusters suspended from jewel-like cartouches on a matted ground.

THIS tazza which was formerly the property of St. Michaels Church, Southampton, is one of the finest early Elizabethan secular examples extant and is the only one recorded with a bowl embossed with figures in the Dutch or German manner. Canon Braithwaite's Church Plate of Hampshire 1909 has two illustrations and he remarks: 'This remarkable tazza is without exception one of the most beautiful pieces of silver work belonging to the Elizabethan period that exists in England'.

*London, 1567/8
Maker's mark,
a bunch of grapes
Height, 5¾ inches
Weight,
23 ounces 1 dwt*

Although the source of design from which the English goldsmith worked, has not yet been identified, the figured bowl can quite certainly be related to the mid-16th Century Flemish and South German pictorial and graphic tradition. Compare with a bronze plaque by H. Jamnitzer of Rebecca and Eleazer at the well based on a woodcut of 1571 by Jost Amman in the small Frankfurter Bible and an unsigned Dordrecht tazza of 1596 (Frederick's 'Dutch Silver' No. 19) based on a similar plaque, in turn made after a print of 1552 by H. Cock after M. Van Heamskerk.

The marine monsters embossed around the foot are an early example of a motif popular with English goldsmiths for well over half a century; compare the Steeple Cup of 1627 (No. 13).

While the date at which this tazza came into Church hands is not recorded it is likely to have been some considerable time after it was made.*

W. J. Connor, formerly Assistant Archivist to Southampton City record office writes:

'An extensive search in the records and elsewhere has failed to produce documentary evidence regarding the early history of the tazza. The ignorance of the 19th Century Churchwardens regarding this piece and the absence of any tradition surrounding it suggest that it has been in the hands of the Church from an early date. The initials A.W., engraved under the foot, do not help in this matter since they cannot be identified with any particular person. It is not therefore possible either
to prove

to prove or refute the theory that this tazza may be attributed to the Wriothesley connection. It should be noted, however, that 1567 was the year when Sir Richard Lyster's wife erected the canopied altar tomb on the north side of the chancel.

Jackson in 'English Goldsmiths and Their Marks' records two other important Elizabethan pieces by the goldsmith who used the bunch of grapes mark. The first is the standing cup and cover of 1568 presented to the Armourers' Company by Florence Caldwell in 1611, illustrated on plate VI in Ellis, 'The Ancient Silver Plate Belonging to The Worshipful Company of Armourers and Brasiers'. The other is another cup and cover, hallmarked 1569, presented to Corpus Christi College, Cambridge by Archbishop Parker, illustrated on Plate LII in Jones, 'The Old Plate of The Cambridge Colleges'. Both these, especially the former, display quality of workmanship and use of Renaissance motifs to be compared with this tazza.

The Flemish connection can be most clearly seen on a Flemish tazza from the second half of the 16th Century at the Art Institute of Chicago.

*It had been used as a credence paten, and was supposed, from its colour, to have been brass, and of little value, until the visit of the Royal Archaeological Institute in 1902, when it was examined by Mr W. Heward Bell F.S.A. and its value recognised.

LENT BY SOUTHAMPTON MUSEUM SERVICE.

Exhibited in the Loan Exhibition, 25 Park Lane, 1929 catalogue No. 790 illustrated pl.VI.
Exhibited Silver Treasures from English Churches, Christies, 1955 Catalogue No. 27, illustrated pl.VIII.

Illustrated and described in E.H. Goddard Archaeological Journal, 1902 Vol. LIX p.326.
Illustrated and described in Jackson History of English Plate p.179ff., fig. 198–200.
Illustrated and described in Braithwaite The Church Plate of Hampshire p.302ff., and two plates.

Plate VIII

Plate IX,
The interior of the shallow bowl depicting the meeting of Isaac and Rebecca.

Plate X,
The initials A.W. engraved under the foot may refer to a member of the family of Wriothesley, Earls of Southampton. There is a monument to a family member Sir Michael Lyster, in St. Michael's Church, Southampton.

Plate XI,
Detail of the underbowl repousse with fruits and
foliage clusters suspended from jewel-like
cartouches on a matted ground.

SILVER gilt spice or dessert plates (two from a set of six engraved dishes) depicting scenes from the stories of Abraham and Isaac. These two plates depict Abraham with three angels and his sacrifice of his son Isaac. Round the central roundels are engraved fantastic sea monsters, oysters, lobsters and mermen. The rims are engraved with three roundels of birds, set between panels in which beasts sit among entwining foliage. A shield on the rim is engraved with a coat-of-arms, probably that of William Montague of Oakley, Bedfordshire, the fifth son of Sir Edward Oakley, Lord Chief Justice (died 1556).

London, 1573/4 Maker's mark, FR in monogram. Engraving attributed to the artist Pover M Diameter, 9¼ inches

SEVERAL sets of such engraved plates have survived. One group of twelve, previously in Horace Walpole's collection at Strawberry Hill and now in the possession of the Dukes of Buccleugh, bears the same goldsmith's mark. The engraved scenes depict another Biblical story, that of the Prodigal Son. While some of the bird roundels on the rims are from the same source as the Montague set, the panels of foliage differ.

Another set, now in the U.S.A., belonging to Messrs. Fowler, with a London hallmark of 1567 and depicting the Labours of Hercules, has borders similar to the Buccleugh set. Both these two groups and a set of twelve plates in the Metropolitan Museum, which lack a hallmark or maker's mark, are signed by the unidentified engraver Pover M in monogram. His treatment of the central scenes varies according to the nature of the source from which they were taken (woodcuts by Bernard Salomon for the Metropolitan Museum set; woodcuts by Heinrich Aldegrave for the Hercules set; another, unidentified set of old testament woodcuts for the Montague set) but the high degree of skill common to all these plates and to other signed pieces enables a firm attribution of the Montague set for this extremely skilled, foreign, engraver, working in London in the late 1560s and early 1570s. The signed ewer and basin of 1567, now at the Boston Museum of Fine Art, and another unsigned set of 1575 bear the marks of two more London goldsmiths.

LENT BY THE VICTORIA AND ALBERT MUSEUM.

Sold by a member of the Montague family *at* Christies 3rd July, 1946.
J.F. Hayward Virtuoso Goldsmiths and the Triumph of Mannerisms 1540–1620 *London 1976, p.402, pl.660.*

Charles Oman English Engraved Silver *p.37–46. Appendix I. pl.38, 39.*
Charles Oman and Jonathan Mayne Six Elizabethan Gilt Plates *Burlington Magazine Vol. LXXXVIII 1946 p.184–7.*

Plate XII

Plate XIII, Abraham with three angels.

Plate XIV, Abraham and his sacrifice of his son, Isaac.

TANKARD, parcel-gilt of tapering outline with engraved decoration to the body, the chased strapwork derives from the wooden canns and water containers widely used in Northern Europe in the 16th century. The base and lid embossed with flowers and foliage typical of English Elizabethan tankards.

London, 1579/80
Maker's mark, I.C.
with eagle's head
between

THE tankard is identifiable as a new type of English drinking vessel from the 1560s. None can be identified in the 1559 inventory of the royal plate and only a small group is listed in the 1574 inventory. Collins discusses the problem of terminology and suggests that some of the vessels described as 'hans-pots' and 'cruses' might also be recognisable as tankards. A characteristic feature is a prominent horizontal moulding below the lip and above the base which recalls the iron bands or binding hoops of the original wooden vessel.

The earliest English hallmarked examples are the two tankards presented by Archbishop Matthew Parker in 1571 to Trinity Hall and Gonville and Caius College, Cambridge; compare also the tankard in the Irwin Untermyer Collection 1585.

LENT FROM THE COLLECTION OF THE WORSHIPFUL COMPANY OF GOLDSMITHS.

Formerly in the collection of Dr. J.B. Ashford sold
19th March, 1889 Lot 140.

Plate XV

THE Westwell silver gilt livery flagons with original gilding. Baluster shaped each on domed bases finely chased with scrolling strapwork enclosing flower heads, Tudor roses and fruit motifs on a matted ground, the spool shaped stem supporting a baluster shaped body similarly decorated with leaf engraved scroll handle, the cover engraved with strapwork motifs and cherub mask thumbpieces.

*London, 1594/5
Maker's mark,
I.M. over a billet,
and the other, 1597/8,
maker's mark,
T.S. over a double-
headed eagle
Height, 11¾ inches*

S OME of the finest of the surviving Tudor secular plate belongs to small English parish churches. The number of such pieces is from time to time reduced, as the churches are forced to dispose of them, in order to cover the cost of structural repairs.

Although differing in date and in small details of decoration, these flagons are obviously intended as a pair.

There are only 23 examples of these vessels known to be extant. Originally secular, they were used in Tudor times for replenishing cups at City Livery Companies', and other banquets. When these passed out of fashion, they were occasionally presented for ecclesiastical use as communion flagons.

The Reformation of the Church of England had led to a wholesale destruction of the medieval plate. The communion cup and paten constituted the minimum requirement for the service of the altar in the English Protestant Church. However, the considerable quantity of communion wine consumed when the whole congregation partook meant a further requirement of a pair of flagons. In 1621 William Laud, later Archbishop, attempted to regulate the forms of Anglican worship, in particular by insisting on the use of decent vessels for the communion. This campaign resulted in the poor Kentish community of Westwell asking the help of their Lord of the Manor. According to a Church Register entry of 1630 these flagons were given by George Baker, Lord of the Manor of Ripple in the parish of Westwell, who, 'seeing all went into the City and none into the Temple (where, because he had found great consolation, he desired to make some poor oblation) gave to this Church two guilt flagons and guilt cuppe with a cover.'

LENT FROM THE COLLECTION OF THE WORSHIPFUL COMPANY OF GOLDSMITHS.

Provenance Vicar and Churchwardens of
Westwell Church, Kent.

Sold by Sotheby & Co. 4th July 1968, Lot 98.

Plate XVI

AN Elizabeth I silver gilt cup and cover of unusually large size and superb quality; the cone-shaped bowl engraved with a series of shells with lozenges between and with a blank cartouche reserved for a coat-of-arms which, for some reason, was never engraved. The double-domed cover similarly engraved rising to a baluster urn-shaped finial. The baluster stem, which lies between two ornamental collars, is set with three Tudor roses and rests on a small and delicately engraved foot with two bands of ovolo work.

ALTHOUGH the cup has never been engraved with arms, we can suggest for whom it was originally made. The cup has descended in the Wolryche and Gatacre families until the present day. Another clue, however, is the shells engraved all over the bowl and cover. In Renaissance times, the shell was the sign of birth as seen in Botticelli's 'Birth of Venus' where she is shown being pulled ashore by sea-horses, standing in a shell and holding another shell in her hand. One can reasonably say, therefore, that the cup was a christening present and, given this fact, it would seem more than likely to suppose that it was a christening present to Thomas Wolryche Esq., of Dudmaston, grandson of John Wolryche, who married Mary, 'the fair maid of Gatacre', daughter of John Gatacre. He was the son of Francis Wolryche and was baptised at Worfield on the 27th March, 1598, the year of the making of this cup. The family originally came from Cheshire but acquired the estate of Dudmaston in Shropshire in the 12th century, the Deed of Grant being one of the oldest private deeds in England.

Thomas Wolryche was educated at Cambridge where he studied geometry, history and heraldry. He was admitted to the Inner Temple in 1615 and, afterwards, represented the Borough of Much Wenlock in the parliaments of 1621, 1624 and 1625. During the outbreak of the Civil War, he was Captain of the Militia and Deputy Lieutenant for the county of Shropshire, and, at his own expense, he raised a regiment of which he was Colonel. Contemporaries spoke of 'the lofty majesty of his person' and, further, 'that to his pre-eminent skill in heraldry, he added the more solid studies of history and mathematics'. The King appointed him to the post of Governor of Bridgnorth and, on the 22nd July 1641, he was knighted at Whitehall and the following month was created a Baronet. For his unbending loyalty during these wars, he suffered severely, being twice sequestered and more than once thrown into prison.

Thomas Wolryche died on the 4th July, 1668, and was buried at the Wolryche Chapel at St. Andrews Church, Quatt. He had married in
1625,

London, 1598/9
Fully marked on lid and bowl,
Maker's mark, IE, possibly one of the family of Eccleston, sometimes Egleston; John Egleston, alias Eccleston, was practising as a goldsmith in 1570.
Height, 16½ inches
Weight, 36 ounces

1625, Ursula, daughter of Thomas Ottley of Pitchford, by whom he had twelve children, of whom four sons and three daughters survived him.

The Baronetcy became extinct in 1723 on the death of his great-grandson, Sir Thomas Wolryche, the estate eventually passing to the Wolryche-Whitmores. Much of the estate, including a great deal of the silver, reverted to the Gatacre family and this present cup was the property of the late Galfry William Gatacre.

PRIVATE LOAN.

Exhibited Victoria and Albert Museum. *Compare* a standing cup and cover *at* S. Mary Abbotts, Kensington: 1599/60, *maker's mark* a squirrel. *Now lacking cover. Freshfield* The Communion Plate of the County of London.

Compare a standing cup *exhibited at* the Fitzwilliam Museum, Cambridge *1975 (ref SC12):* 1608/9, *maker's mark* TC *with* three pellets above, one *below.*
Compare J. Starkie Gardner F.S.A. Old Silver Work From 15th to 18th Centuries. *Loan collection 1902. pl. 53.*

Plate XVII

A SILVER gilt cup and cover, the bowl and cover are decorated with bands of delicate scrolling and interlaced foliage with berries applied in relief to a matted ground, alternating on the body with finely engraved hunting scenes. The stem and finial are in vase form.

London, 1611/12
Maker's mark, TYL
in monogram
Height, 21 inches

THIS egg-shaped cup is an outstanding example of a small group of pieces with closely comparable filigree scrollwork decoration, attributed to this goldsmith. Only this and a virtually identical standing cup of the same year bear a maker's mark and date letter; this second cup was presented to Christ's College, Cambridge in 1919. Among the other unmarked pieces are a rock-crystal cup and cover, given to Tong Church in Shropshire in 1629; a salt, in the Duke of Bedford's collection; and a caster in the Victoria and Albert Museum. It has been suggested on grounds of style that there were two goldsmiths with the same initials, probably father and son; the quality of the engraving and the technique employed in the ornament, unparalleled in other work of the period by English goldsmiths, suggest that this was the mark of an immigrant goldsmith, trained in Germany or the Low Countries.

LENT BY THE VICTORIA AND ALBERT MUSEUM.

Charles Oman English Silversmiths Work *pl.37*
J.F. Hayward Virtuoso Goldsmiths *p.34 pl.663.*
Sir Charles Jackson A History of English Plate
Illustrated *Vol.II p.669 Fig 878.*

Plate XVIII,
Engraving, delicate scrolling and
interlaced foliage.

Plate XIX

A GOLD Portrait Medallion of Queen Elizabeth I the obverse showing a three-quarters facing bust of Queen Elizabeth wearing a small crown and richly ornamented dress with ruff. The reverse showing crowned royal arms with supporters and 'DIEU ET MON DROIT' above. Below that there is an inscribed tablet reading:

'QVI LEO DE IVDA EST ET FLOS DE IESSE LEONES PROTEGAR ET FLORES ELIZABETHA IVOS.'

'YOU WHO ARE THE LION OF JUDAH AND THE FLOWER OF JESSE, MAY LIONS AND FLOWERS PROTECT THEE, O ELIZABETH.'

It is signed above the Queen's head Si. Pas. fe. and was made about 1615. The medallion itself is thought to be unique, in gold, and is in a fine gold frame for use as a pendant jewel.

London, 1615–22
Height, 3¼ inches

SIMON de Passe, Crispijn's son and pupil, was born in Cologne about 1595. He worked as an engraver in Utrecht from 1612–1615, in London 1615–1622, in Paris 1623, and after a short stay in Utrecht, moved to Copenhagen in 1624 where he died in 1647. This particular engraving was copied from a miniature by Isaac Oliver which still hangs in Windsor Castle. We can assume that Simon de Passe saw the portrait miniature of Elizabeth I on one of his visits to engrave a member of the Royal household. The very decorative gold frame and faceted glass are believed to be contemporary.

The majority of his portrait medallions engraved during his English period are of members of the Royal family. The designs are almost always copied from other artists.

Closely comparable with these silver portrait medallions are the equivalent of the portrait miniatures of Elizabeth and James which were painted in quite large numbers, these were images presented by the monarch to loyal friends and supporters, to be worn around the neck. Silver examples are normally pierced with a suspension hole, the custom of wearing silver rather than painted miniature portrait medallions was widespread in the Low Countries. The very high degree of detail visible in this medallion indicates that the engraver was producing small numbers of these highly finished objects. He is known also for the sets of die-stamped gaming counters with portraits of English Royalty which were produced for general sale.

It appears that there is longstanding uncertainty regarding the technique he employed; Fredericks discusses this in his volume on Dutch Silver. Due to the existence of a number of examples of one portrait some consider them to have been duplicated by casting or die-

stamping

stamping whereas others feel that it would hardly have been possible to use such fine dies without damaging them immediately, and that therefore they must have been engraved. Fredericks is of the latter opinion. He also points out that there are minute differences between the lettering and other details of portrait medallions when seen under a high-powered microscope and finally that a skilful craftsman would be capable, with the help of a transfer, of making a series of copies of the most striking resemblance.

LENT BY HER MAJESTY QUEEN ELIZABETH II.

Ex. Collection of the late Mrs. Greta S. Heckett.
Ex. Collection of Major-General E.H. Goulburn.
Ex. Pierpont Morgan Collection.

Discussed in Hind History of Engraving in England *Vol. II.*
Fredericks Dutch Silver *Vol. II.*

Plate XX, Front, portrait of Queen Elizabeth I

Plate XXI, Reverse, royal coat-of-arms.

A PAIR of silver wine cups of great boldness being larger than usual campana shaped, each on spreading feet with strong baluster stem, the plain bowl engraved 'the guift of Mr Anthony Risbie Gent'. They are further engraved on the underside of the foot 'Barnards Ine'. The arms are those of Risbie of Co. Suffolk.

London, 1627/8
Maker, Walter Shute
Maker's mark,
a bow and arrow
between W.S.
Height, 10½ inches

BARNARD'S Inn and Staple Inn were two inns of chancery which belonged to Gray's Inn. These prestigious establishments go back to about the year 1415 and were, so to speak, the preliminary educational establishments attended by a young lawyer before entering the Inns of Court.

By about 1553 the Inns of Court began to differentiate between barristers and attorneys; the rigid demarcation between the two had far-reaching circumstances. Those who sought their education in the Inns of Court looked beyond the Inns of Chancery which eventually fell into decline, and their sites were put to more profitable use. Barnard's Inn was sold to the Mercers Company in about 1884.

The custom of presenting a piece of plate on rising to the senior levels of an institution was common to the city livery companies, the ancient colleges of Oxford and Cambridge and the Inns of Court and Chancery. The historic plate collections of these institutions are largely composed of such gifts.

PRIVATE LOAN.

Exhibited Brand Inglis a Loan Exhibition of Silver
1978.
Compare a further example by the same maker dated
1625, Merchant Adventurers Company, York and
illustrated by Charles Oman Caroline Silver pl. 6a.

Plate XXII,
Underside of the foot, engraved 'Barnards Ine'.

Plate XXIII

THE Romney Steeple Cup, the foot, bowl and cover are chased and shallowly embossed with dolphins among waves; the bowl is engraved with representations of the town and mayoralty seals of New Romney, Kent, the first depicting a ship in sail and the second three lions passant gardant, the arms borne by each of the Cinque Ports. The foot is inscribed 'Ricardus Godfreius Thomas filius servitii sui ergo, in tribus novissimis parliamentis accepit 1 Jan. 1627.' The bowl is inscribed 'Summa Cato, Medium Cicero, dat Apicius vinum.'

London, 1627/8
Maker's mark, F
Height, 23 inches

AS the latin inscription records, the cup was presented by the town of Romney to Richard Godfrey, who sat for the borough in three of King James' parliaments. Representations of institutional seals on plate often are an indication of a completed term of office; the office-holder commissioned the piece as a souvenir, incorporating not only the design but often also the metal, of the seal concerned. See for example the earliest surviving seal cups, one in the British Museum and one in the Victoria and Albert Museum made for Sir Nicholas Bacon from his Exchequer seal in 1574. The Walpole Salver is a particularly grand and finely-executed example of this custom (Cat no. 36). However, in this instance the town presumably commissioned the goldsmith to add the engraving of the seals simply as the most appropriate reference to Godfrey's long official association. A new mayoralty seal was cut in 1614 and both seals were inspected and approved on a heraldic visitation of Kent in 1619; there is no reference to a further recutting.

LENT BY THE VICTORIA AND ALBERT MUSEUM.

Charles Oman English Silversmiths Work *pl.46.*
N.M. Penzer An Index of Steeple Cups *Society of Silver Collectors 1962.*

Plate XXIV,
Detail of Cup showing engraving of Romney Town seal, also three characteristically chased dolphins and scollop shells can be seen.

Plate XXV

FLAGON, chased and embossed overall with floral scrollwork enclosing two cartouches chased with a dolphin and a sea monster, framed in the auricular style. The beaded hollow handle terminates in a flat plate bearing a cherub.

Engraved with the arms granted in 1687 to Frances Tyssen (1622–1699) a merchant from Flushing who settled in London and became naturalized in 1657; the arms were subsequently concealed under a plain silver panel, presumably by a later owner. This flagon is one of a pair formerly in use at All Saints Church, Thirkleby, Yorkshire; the other is now at Temple Newsam House, Leeds. These are secular flagons given later for communion wine, see the entry for the Deane Cup (No. 3) for other examples.

London, 1646/7
Maker's Mark,
a hound sejant
Height, 10¼ inches

FEW English goldsmiths found customers eager to pay for elaborate embossing and chasing during the Civil War and Commonwealth period; a more fully integrated example of the auricular ornament by this maker is to be seen on the 1666 porringer at Wadham College, Oxford. The hound sejant was the most distinguished English goldsmith working in the mid-seventeenth century. He was also responsible, in the same year, for a closely comparable pair, now in the Irwin Untermyer collection in the Metropolitan Museum. While the purchasers of these flagons cannot be identified, his customers included several prominent royalists for whom he made church plate in the revived Gothic style between 1646 and 1666.

LENT BY THE VICTORIA AND ALBERT MUSEUM.

Exhibited Christies Silver Treasures from English Churches *1955.*   *Charles Oman* Caroline Silver *p. 280 no. 31a.*

Plate XXVI

SALVER, on foot, engraved in the centre with a contemporary coat-of-arms below a figurative mantling, a crested helmet above. The highly unusual raised border repoussé and chased with a band of flowers, fruit and leafage on a matted ground, the scolloped edge with punched shell motifs standing on a spreading capstan foot.

London, 1657/8
by Arthur Manwaring
Weight,
46 ounces 17dwt
Diameter,
15½ inches

THE Arms are those of Chester of Amesbury Co. Gloucester, probably for Thomas Chester (late of Gloucester) Citizen and Merchant Tailor of London and Captain of Trained Bands. He married Mary, daughter and heir of Thomas Dorbar of St. Thomas the Apostle London in 1647. He died in 1670.

Arthur Manwaring completed his apprenticeship with William Tyler in 1643. In May 1664 the wardens of the Goldsmiths Company decided to remake a group of plate which had been melted down in 1637. Arthur Manwaring received an ingot of silver with which to make two of the pieces, one of which is now in the collection of the Goldsmiths Company; Plate 3a 'Caroline Silver' by Charles Oman.

PRIVATE LOAN.

Provenance The Honourable Pererine Fairfax.
Michael Clayton The Collectors' Dictionary of Silver and Gold *No. 455.*
Charles Oman Caroline Silver *pl.19A p.30.*
Exhibited Brand Inglis a Loan Exhibition of Silver, 1978.

Compare another silver-gilt porringer and salver with a further unusual border:
Arthur Manwaring; *London* 1655/6; *Weight,* 43 ounces 17dwt.
Provenance George Bowler Gipps 1930.
William Randolph Hearst 1938.

Plate XXVII

A SALVER and Porringer, both pieces finely embossed with hunting scenes and auricular ornament, and engraved with a contemporary coat-of-arms, those borne by Anthony Ashley-Cooper (1621-1683) between 1661 when he was created Baron Ashley and 1672 when he was raised to be Earl of Shaftesbury. The salver depicts four episodes in a boar hunt, the continuous design divided up by trees on hillocks; two riders pause while deciding their direction; a man lies gored on his broken pole; a hornblowing footman disturbs a deer while the boar watches and a huntsman closes in for the kill. The porringer depicts a rider and three spear-carrying footmen hunting a stag and hounds coursing a hare, below a border of fleshy masks in the auricular style. The handles are cast winged demi-figures with serpent-headed terminals. The cover is also embossed with a hunting scene.

Presumably London, circa 1661 Maker's mark only, struck on porringer base and rim of salver, a star above an escallop. Height, 10¼ inches Diameter of salver, 15¼ inches Scratchweight of salver, 50.10 Scratchweight of porringer, 26.10

IT seems probable that this set was a gift from Charles II to Anthony Ashley-Cooper, created Baron Ashley on 20th April 1661, the day of the King's coronation; he served as Chancellor of the Exchequer and Under-Treasurer. Such porringers were among the customary awards at New Year to the great officers of state, which were graded by weight and elaboration according to the rank of the recipient. Several such royal gifts are known, (identified by inscriptions) such as the porringer of 1673 (now lacking its salver) presented by the King to his almoner Richard Sterne, Archbishop, which is in the Victoria and Albert Museum. The same goldsmith was responsible for a large and handsomely-embossed pair of gilt candle-sticks which were included in the 1664 ambassadorial gift presented to the Tsar by the Earl of Carlisle and now in the Kremlin Armouries, Moscow. He was presumably a regular supplier of high-quality plate to the Jewel House.

PRIVATE LOAN.

Charles Oman Caroline Silver pp.39—40, pl.10.

Plate XXVIII

A PARCEL-gilt Cage Cup, the cylindrical body and the cover are encased in silver open-work, chased and embossed with acanthus foliage incorporating an eagle and a peacock. A moulded finial rises from a cast openwork flower; the two cast handles are of a strongly auricular design. The cup stands on three ball and claw feet.

London, 1669/70
Maker's mark,
CG in double monogram,
with a sun
Height, 7⅛ inches

THE decorative effect achieved by setting gilded openwork against a plain burnished body was popular from the Restoration for about thirty years. While a number of goldsmiths used the technique, the finest pieces are from the workshops of a small group who were particularly responsive to contemporary Dutch and German work. Charles Oman suggested that the goldsmith CG monogram sponsored the plate of certain foreign craftsmen; this may account for the distinctive handles, comparable with those on a cagework tankard of about 1670 at the Boston Museum of Fine Art, which is marked by Jacob Bodendick, and a flagon of 1660 made for the Bishop of Durham's chapel by Wolfgang Howzer. The hound sejant maker also adopted a version of this muscular writhing form for the handles of a porringer at Wadham College, Oxford (1666). The cagework designs are from a common Dutch source and may well have been produced by one specialist craftsman. A two-handled cup formerly in the Hearst collection by TM over a crown (1669) incorporates similar birds and the sleeve design on an unmarked cup in the Irwin Untermyer collection, dated to about 1680, is even closer to this example. The technique was occasionally used also on church plate; two chalices, one of 1670 and one of 1676, are partly caged.

LENT BY THE VICTORIA AND ALBERT MUSEUM.

Charles Oman Caroline Silver *p.27.*

E. Hackenbroch English & Other Silver in the Irwin Untermyer Collection *revised 1969, 61.*

Plate XXIX

A SILVER teapot, with tapering body, conical lid and short straight spout; the curved handle set at right angles. The body is engraved with the arms of the East India Company and of George Lord Berkeley who presented it to the Company in 1670; the inscription reads:
'This Silver tea-pott was presented to Ye Comte of ye East India Cumpany by ye Right Honore George Lord Berkeley of Berkeley Castle. A member of that Honourable and worthy society and A true Hearty Lover of them 1670.'

London, 1670/1
Maker's Mark, T.L.
Height, 13½ inches

THE conical form of this teapot is close to the shape adopted, perhaps from contemporary Turkish brassware, for coffee pots; this may be compared with the rather smaller silver coffee pot hallmarked 1681 which Richard Sterne presented to the East India Company, also in the Museum. The Company was heavily involved in importing, and hence promoting the consumption of the new beverages; the arrival of coffee, tea, and chocolate in the mid-17th Century substantially changed the English way of life during the reign of Charles II. Samuel Pepys, 1633–1703 wrote in his diary for 28th September 1660:–
'I sent for a cup of tea (the Chinese beverage) which I never drunk before.'

The coffee houses, where tea was also sold, soon became meeting places for representatives of literary, political and other circles, hence promoting the consumption of the new beverages.

LENT BY THE VICTORIA AND ALBERT MUSEUM.

Charles Oman Caroline Silver pp 57–8, pl.70A.

Plate XXX

Plate XXXI, Coat-of-arms and inscription.

A PAIR of Tankards of plain barrel outline standing on three feet formed as eagles with heads turned to the right, the body decorated with applied cord bands, the auricular handles cast and highly embossed with cord work. Engraved with a contemporary coat of arms in plume mantling for Sir Thomas Langham father of the 1st Countess of Warrington.

London, 1671/2 by Thomas Jenkins Height, 9⅝ inches

AN interesting comparison regarding the feet and finial occurs in the two-handled parcel gilt cup and cover exhibited at The Exhibition of the Historic Plate of the City of London at Goldsmiths Hall 1951. The use of animals for feet also occurs in the form of lions on The Drapers Company Tankard London 1661, maker's mark DR below a coronet. A further example is in the Irwin Untermeyr collection, a silver gilt tankard London 1668, maker's mark IN. The handle is reminiscent of the work of Jacob Bodendick, for example, a cage work tankard in the Museum of Fine Arts Boston.

An article appeared in the Daily Telegraph, following the Foley Grey sale on 20th April, 1921, which is reproduced here in full, you will note that the 1671 Tankards are mentioned as well as the Philip Rollos 1701 Wine Cistern (*No. 29*).

'Not even in the Ashburnham collection of silver sold just before the war, was there to be seen such an array of plates and utensils for table use as appeared yesterday at Christies in the seventeenth and eighteenth century silver belonging to Catherine Lady Grey and Sir John Foley Grey. There was indeed a stage in the sale when twelve dozen plain dinner plates (engraved with the arms of George Booth, second Earl of Warrington) fetched nearly £4,000 and Mr S.J. Phillips the purchaser, a little while before, gave nearly £1,400 for three dozen of similar provenance. It is safe to assume that the bulk of this Grey collection realising over £32,000 will be eventually shipped to America. The total astonished many people, especially as the aggregate for the three days' dispersal of the Ashburnham silver in 1914 was £40,288 only. A set of six George II sconces, embossed with classical figures, by Peter Archambo, 1730 brought the highest sum of the day, £3,100 (Permain). These had the engraved monogram and coronet of the second Earl of Warrington already mentioned, from whom much of the collection originally was derived. Next, Mr Lionel Crichton paid £2,000 for a 1754 toilet service by Magdalen Felin, and engraved with the arms of Harry, fourth Earl of Stamford, and his wife, Lady Mary Booth; an earlier toilet service, by Issac Liger, 1728 bringing £1,350 (Loudoun). The highest price per ounce was 370 shillings (Wilson) for a pair of Charles II

tankards

tankards by T. Issod, 1671, weighing 102 oz, £1,857 [These are the Jenkins tankards]. The heaviest single piece was the last lot, a plain oval wine-cistern, by Peter Archambo, with the Warrington arms, weighing 1,124 oz, which was one of the few bargains in the sale at 15s.6d an ounce, £871.2s (Crichton).

A huge tea-urn, 27 in high, and weighing 575 oz, suitable for any reconciliation party, another Archambo-Warrington composite, was another modest affair at 10s an ounce, £287.10s (Pearson). A pair of George II, cups and covers, on the other hand, of the same make and engraving, realised £722.2s (Wilson), at 120s an ounce; and two jugs and covers, by Paul de Lamerie, 1732, with the Warrington crest, £1,013.10s (Crichton) at 100s. A Phil Rollos, 1701 oval Wine cistern brought £1,750 at 125s (Grant), and among numerous soap boxes was one by Lewis Mettayer, weighing nearly 8 oz, which fetched 100s an ounce, £39.15s (Crichton). Even a table-bell, 1729, cost over £86, at 210s an ounce (Tessier).'

LENT BY THE NATIONAL TRUST, DUNHAM MASSEY.

Compare a two-handled parcel gilt cup and cover *exhibited at* The Exhibition of the Historic Plate of the City of London *Goldsmiths Hall, 1951. Illustrated* Goldsmiths Plate *pl. 41.*

Compare the Drapers Company Tankard, *illustrated in Charles Oman* Caroline Silver 1625–1688, *pl. 28b.*

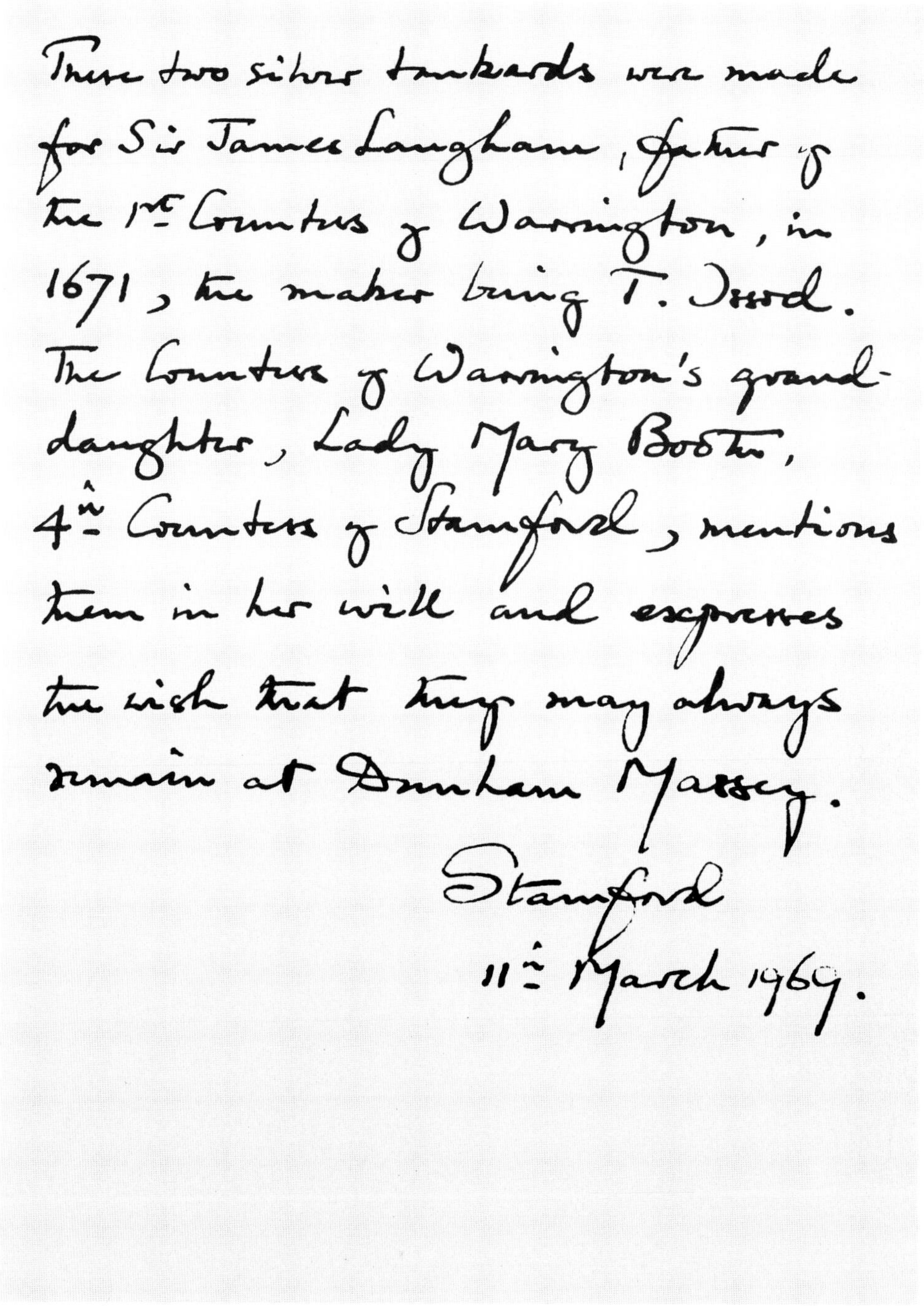

These two silver tankards were made
for Sir James Langham, father of
the 1st Countess of Warrington, in
1671, the maker being T. Issod.
The Countess of Warrington's grand-
daughter, Lady Mary Booth,
4th Countess of Stamford, mentions
them in her will and expresses
the wish that they may always
remain at Dunham Massey.

Stamford
11th March 1969.

Plate XXXII
Note found inside one of the Tankards
They were sold in 1921 as part of the Foley-Grey
Collection and brought back to Dunham Massey
by 10th Earl of Stamford to honour his forbear's
wishes.

Plate XXXIII

A TWO handled porringer and cover of bombé form chased with a broad band of flowers, foliage and animals, the cover similarly chased and surmounted with a quadruple mask finial, the caryatid scroll handles of bold design.

London, 1672/3 by John Ruslin
Height, 8½ inches

AT least at Court the porringer had emerged about a century earlier as a vessel in which an individual portion of some nourishing mixture of egg, milk, grain and alcohol was served.

In 1576 Queen Elizabeth commissioned from the goldsmith, Hugh Kayle, an octagonal porringer weighing 25oz. A year later she was given a slightly lighter porringer 'standing upon an oaken leaf, with a snake upon the toppe', a form recognisably related to the earliest surviving Stuart examples. The rigidity of formal dining arrangements encouraged people to take quick light meals in their chambers: the porringer, a covered vessel, which could be used to cook and to serve such light meals retained its popularity until cooking and dining habits changed under French influence late in the 17th Century.

This porringer is a particularly handsome example of the most familiar post-Restoration form although bands of embossed animals among flowers are found in porringers of the 1650s.

John Ruslin was one of the goldsmiths supplying plate to the Jewel House and thus numbered among his clients discriminating patrons anxious to buy plate in the finest current style: his skill is apparent both in the quality of the embossing and in the hint of the auricular design to be seen in the finial.

PRIVATE LOAN.

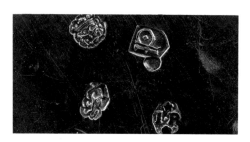

J. Starkie Gardner Old Silverwork Chiefly English from the 15th to 18th Century, Loan Collection Exhibited 1902. *Pl.65 fig. 1 shows a very similar* porringer and cover *of the same size dated* 1666 *and lent by* Sir Charles Welby.
Sir Charles Jackson, History of English Plate, *vol. II Chapter 24.*

Plate XXXIV, Hallmarks.

Plate XXXV

THE Edmund Bury Godfrey Flagon engraved with the arms of Charles II and those of Sir Edmund Bury Godfrey and with inscriptions in Latin flanking plaques which depict the burial of London Plague victims in 1665 and the Great Fire of London in 1666. The spout is a later addition, to enable the flagon to be more easily used as a jug.

THE flagon is one of a group of pieces, comprising this flagon and six tankards similar in design and with the same engraved details. All but one tankard bear the date letter for 1675 and are by the same maker; the sixth was made by another goldsmith two years earlier. These were distributed by Sir Edmund among his friends to recall the honours conferred on him by Charles II; each is engraved 'Ex Dono EBG' and one, now on loan to the Victoria and Albert Museum, has descended in the family of its recipient, Thomas Lamplugh, Archbishop of York.

London, 1675/6 Maker's mark, IN with a mullet below in a heart Height, 12¾ inches

Sir Edmund Bury Godfrey (1621–1678) was a merchant and well-known Justice of the Peace for Westminster. For his notable assiduity in relieving distress during the Plague and Fire, Charles II honoured him with a knighthood in September 1666 and a massive 800-ounce gift of white plate was authorized by warrant to the Jewel house on 17th October 1666. This royal gift is referred to in the Latin inscription as an 'oenophora' or wine container and presumably provided the metal for the smaller and more practical commemorative vessels later commissioned by Sir Edmund.

Charles Oman suggested that the vessel might have been a wine cistern but a reference in Samuel Pepys' diary on 1st May 1667 suggests that an exceptionally large flagon may be more likely. 'My seeing at Sir Robert Viners (the Royal Goldsmith) 2 or 3 great silver flagons made with inscriptions as gifts of the King to such and such persons of quality as did stay in Town the late great Plague for the keeping of things in order.'

Godfrey was found dead on Primrose Hill on the outskirts of London in October 1678. He was popularly believed to have been murdered by Roman Catholics who were anxious to revenge themselves on him for having taken the depositions of Titus Oates (1649–1705) relating to the spurious 'Popish Plot.'

This was alleged to threaten the lives of Charles II and of his Protestant subjects in order to re-establish Roman Catholic rule in England; Oates was one of the leading fabricators of the story. Before his perjury was discovered, thirty five people had been tried and executed for their complicity as a result of his testimony. The flagon *was formerly* was formerly in the collection of the Earl of Lonsdale, with a Godfrey tankard by the same maker, now also owned by the Farmers' Company.

LENT BY THE WORSHIPFUL COMPANY OF FARMERS.

Roger Lushington The Tankards of Sir Edmund Bury Godfrey.

Godfrey Connoisseur *CXC 1975 pp. 258–265.* *Charles Oman* English Engraved Silver *pp. 65–66, pp. 72–73.*

Plate XXXVI

CHALICE and Paten, the octagonal stem with an acanthus-embossed knot rises from an octagonal foot also embossed with acanthus; there is cut-card work under the bowl and on the paten. The bowl is engraved with the arms of Stephens of Epsom, probably for Anthony Stephens, Esq, who died in 1695.

London, 1675/6 Maker's mark overstruck on bowl, a cinquefoil between IB, a crescent with pellets below for Jacob Bodendick Height, 9⅜ inches Diameter of Paten cover, 8¼ inches

THIS handsome Chalice and Paten, by one of the leading Restoration goldsmiths, is a later example of the taste for Church plate in the 'Gothic style', which had been stimulated by Bishop Lancelot Andrewes (1555–1626) from about 1620. High Church Anglicans, who were often also members of court circles, preferred the revived pre-Reformation form for their liturgical plate. The earliest example is an undated chalice at St. Johns College, Cambridge, given before 1620; other cups of this type from St. Mary Lambeth (1638) and Staunton Harold (1640) may be seen at the Victoria and Albert Museum and several were made for private chapels during the Interregnum. At the time of the Restoration several goldsmiths were commissioned to supply chalices in this style for the royal chapels at St. James and Whitehall Palaces. Between 1671 and 1680 Bodendick supplied several chalices in the Gothic style, notably a closely comparable example of 1676/7 presented by Walter Chetwynd to Ingestre Church, Staffordshire, after it was rebuilt by Christopher Wren.

It is not known by whom the chalice and paten cover was presented to St. Andrew Kingswood, although it is most likely to have been a member of the Stephens family; knifemarks on the paten indicate that bread rather than wafers was used at the communion service, as was customary before the Tractarian revival of the mid-19th century.

LENT BY THE RECTOR AND CHURCHWARDENS OF ST. ANDREW KINGSWOOD, SURREY.

Charles Oman English Church Plate pp. 205–7, 209.

T.S. Cooper Church Plate of Surrey p. 245 and facing page.

Plate XXXVII

A SILVER gilt flagon standing on circular moulded foot chased with acanthus leaves, the body elaborately embossed and chased with swags of flowers and cherub heads on a matted ground, the double scroll handle decorated with foliage, the lid chased and embossed and surmounted by a cross, with a feathered thumb piece.

*London, 1683/4
by* Ralph Leake
Height, 14½ inches

FROM a set of one large and two small flagons, four chalices and patens, a standing paten and a large arms dish given to the Church of St. James Piccadilly by Sir George Geere at the time of its dedication in 1683. The goldsmith, Ralph Leake the elder, was probably the most skilled of the Restoration goldsmiths and numbered several courtiers as well as the Jewel House among his clients. This outstanding set of plate was presented to the newly built church serving the court and suburb of St. James's Palace. The lavish ornament and its size are unusual even for Ralph Leake. The set of plate for Chelsea Hospital Chapel 1688 and for the neighbouring parish of St. Margaret's Westminster 1694 presented by Sarah Dowager Duchess of Somerset is rather more austere.

The bulbous jug form of this flagon is an interesting post-Restoration development occasionally adapted by goldsmiths in preference to the traditional straight-sided flagon for communion wine; a further example at Easton Maundint Church, Northamptonshire of 1672 by I.D in monogram is closely comparable in form.

LENT BY THE VICAR AND CHURCHWARDENS OF ST. JAMES PICCADILLY.

Freshfield Communion Plate in the County of London *1895 p.58.*

Charles Oman English Church Plate *pp.222–3.*

Plate XXXVIII

OBLONG Casket from the Calverley toilet service on scroll and foliage feet, the sides chased with putti vases and scrolling foliage, the cover chased with floral borders and a mythological scene.

London, 1683/4
Maker's mark,
WF *with* a knot.
Length, 9¾ inches

THE full toilet service bequeathed in 1879 by Sir Walter Calverley Trevelyan of Warrington Down, consists of a mirror, a pair of salvers, a pair of oblong caskets (one of these, stolen in the 19th Century, has been replaced by an electrotype) two pairs of round boxes of different sizes, a pair of bowls and covers, a pair of pounce pots and a pin-cushion embossed and chased with acanthus foliage and putti. The original lining, presumably a wooden frame covered with fabric, has not survived so that the function of the casket, whether for jewels or cosmetic tools, cannot now be determined. The lid is set with a cast plaquette of Venus and Adonis (detail, inset), adapted from a plaquette modelled by Jakob Cornelisz Cobaert (d.1615) after designs by the Roman artist Guglielmo della Porta which is not in itself surprising. The original wax models were stolen from the artist's studio and bronze or terracotta casts were offered all over Europe for the use of goldsmiths. The most unusual feature of the plaquettes so far identified in the Calverley service is that only the left-hand part of the original design was used.

Silver toilet services were in use before Charles II was restored to the throne in 1660, but complete services appear to be a development of his reign, reflecting the taste for conspicuous consumption in the form of silver furniture. The toilet service of which this oblong casket forms a part was acquired secondhand by Sir Walter Calverley on the occasion of his marriage to Julia Blackett on 7th January 1706-7. He noted in his diary:

'I and my mother were at cost of a fine set of dressing plate for my wife, which (came to 116L old money)'.

A closely comparable toilet service, made by the same goldsmith in the same year with the gilding restored, was recently sold in New York (Christies 26th October, 1982 Lot 53). The plaques on that service depict scenes from Ovid's Metamorphoses, with acanthus and floral borders chased in a virtually identical style.

LENT BY THE VICTORIA AND ALBERT MUSEUM.

Charles Oman Caroline Silver *pp.18,19,63.*
Michael Clayton The Collectors' Dictionary of Silver and Gold *No.674.*

Surtees Society 1886 Yorkshire Diaries and Biographies of the 17th and 18th Centuries. *Diary of Sir Walter Calverley, p.115.*

Plate XXXIX

SPOUTED *skillet of plain outline standing on three ball and claw feet engraved with a contemporary coat of arms, the spout and lid also plain and the saucepan handle of wood.*

The arms are of Naylor of Offord Darcy, Co. Huntingdon, impaling Pelham.

London, 1685/6
Maker's Mark, I.S.,
cinquefoil *below*
Height, 9¼ inches
to tip of handle

SPOUTED skillets are rare objects; a similar example is in the Irwin Untermyer Collection called a cordial pot, unmarked circa 1690, maker's mark FS beneath a crown. Both are clearly made for the purpose of heating liquid in fairly small quantities, derived from the contemporary French form. The three-foot example occurs occasionally well into the 18th century e.g. on early pieces by Kandler, but English customers appear to have preferred the stable alternative of a flat bottom for their saucepans.

LENT FROM THE COLLECTION OF THE WORSHIPFUL COMPANY OF GOLDSMITHS.

E. Hackenbroch English & Other Silver in the
Irwin Untermyer Collection *revised 1969, 61.*

Plate XL

A WINE Cistern of oval bulging shape applied with cast vertical panels of alternate leaves and husks, cast lions masks clasp the handles; the oval collet foot with spiral gadrooning attached to the body by six nuts and bolts. Engraved with a later coat-of-arms for Sir Nathaniel Curzon, Bart, later Baron Scarsdale, impaling those of his wife Caroline Colyear.

London, 1698/9
by Ralph Leake
Height, 8½ inches
Width, 22 inches

THIS cistern, or cooler, with its pair, now at the Goldsmiths Company were formerly at Kedleston Hall, Derby and formed a set with a fountain by Ralph Leake and another earlier French fountain (now at the Paul Getty Museum). Kedleston was rebuilt between 1759 and 1765 by Nathaniel Curzon; the acquisition of the group of massive dining room plate may be dated approximately by the form of the Curzon arms. Sir Nathaniel succeeded to the baronetcy in 1758 and was elevated to the peerage in 1761. In keeping with the neoclassical form which Adam was giving to both the house and its interiors, the dining room plate was commissioned, from Philips Garden and others, with appropriately Roman ornament; presumably the restrained baroque use of classical motifs on these late Stuart cisterns was regarded as being harmonious. A sketch of Adam's scheme for the dining room shows them arranged in the niche. The purchase of such antique plate, personalized by the added arms, was customary from the early 18th century, particularly where a large quantity of metal was concerned, and a number of late Stuart cistern and fountain sets with later arms are known. The form may be compared with the cistern made by Pierre Harache in 1697, later presented by Queen Anne to the Barber Surgeons Company.

Cisterns were known in the 16th Century but their greatest popularity was during the late Stuart period of ostentatious silver furniture. They were customarily filled with ice to act as coolers for wine but are also referred to, and depicted as massive washing bowls for glasses. A French engraving of c.1695 shows a lady of fashion washing herself in one.

LENT BY THE VICTORIA AND ALBERT MUSEUM.

Charles Oman Caroline Silver *p.46.*

Plate XLI

A PAIR of William III silver gilt ewers and a basin. The helmet shaped ewers on cast gadrooned spreading foot, with similarly cast compressed circular knop, the lower part of the body with alternate applied cut-card flutes and palm leaves, with a plain band above and a gadrooned band beneath the cast and chased lip of stylised shell and scroll motifs, the scroll handles with applied bead rat-tails, capped by a leaf and with further cut-card ornaments below junction, engraved with a coat of arms amidst drapery mantling.

The large circular basin with cast borders of alternate convex and concave flutes the coat of arms finely engraved within a baroque cartouche and ermine mantle surmounted by an Earl's coronet and supported by winged putti.

ALTHOUGH by the late 17th Century the use of the ewer and basin as plate for the dining room decreased they continued to be an essential element of the sideboard display in the grand baroque interior and were normally supplied in pairs.

London, 1699/1700
Maker, Benjamin Pyne
Height of Ewers,
11 inches
Diameter of Basin,
24¾ inches

The arms are those of Grey with Lucas in pretence for Anthony (Grey) Earl of Kent, 1st surviving son and heir born on 11th June 1645, known as Lord Grey until he succeeded to the title in 1651. At the funeral of Mary II he was one of the six supporters of the pall and at the coronation of Queen Anne on 23rd April 1702, was bearer of one of the three swords of state. He married on 2nd March 1662, Mary, only child of John Lucas, 1st Baron Lucas of Shenfield, who was called 'The Good Countess' for her charitable donations. He died suddenly on the 19th August, 1702. His widow died three months later on 1st November 1702.

The exceptional engraving on the basin and ewer can confidently be placed within the corpus of an as yet unidentified engraver recognised by the late Charles Oman and dubbed by him 'The Master of George Vertue'. Oman (English Engraved Silver 1150–1900, London, 1978. pp. 61–63) comments as follows:

'It is possible to recognise his mannerisms on a number of pieces... made at the end of the seventeenth Century. His armorial supporters are shown with the feet resting safely upon a bracket whereas most engravers showed them supported on nothing more substantial than a scroll which bore the motto... (Although attempts have been made to attribute this engraving to Simon Gribelin), it seems wiser to attribute it to a shadowy character mentioned by Horace Walpole in his bibliographical note on George Vertue who was born in 1683 and at "about the age of thirteen was placed with a master who engraved arms on plate and had the chief business in London; but who being extravagant and *broke*

broke, returned to his own country France, after Vertue had served him between three and four years. As the man was unfortunate, though by his own fault, the good nature of the scholar has concealed his name".'

PRIVATE COLLECTION.

Provenance Anthony Grey 11th Earl of Kent.
Sold by The De Grey family Trust 1982.
Exhibited Daily Telegraph Art Treasures Exhibition Olympia 1928.
Exhibited Loan Exhibition, Park Lane 1929 No. 663.

J.F. Hayward Huguenot Silver in England pp.43–45.
Charles Oman English Engraved Silver 1150–1900 pp.61–63.

Plate XLII

Plate XLIII The Grey Ewer.

Plate XLIV. The coat-of-arms and supports.

SLEEVE sugar caster barrel shaped on spreading foot with gadroon edge above pierced and beaded rim, the plain body decorated with a reeded band and the cover pierced and engraved with cherubs, birds and foliage surmounted by cut-card work and a gadrooned knop.

London, 1699/1700 by Pierre Harache II *Height,* 9¼ inches

DEVELOPMENT of the sugar plantations in the West Indies during the seventeenth century meant that sugar, though still expensive, was much more plentiful in late Stuart England than it had been at the beginning of the century. Large cylindrical casters, of 'lighthouse' type, often appeared in sets of three, one large caster for sugar, and a pair of smaller ones for pepper and dry mustard, as standard items of dining table plate.

Persecution following the Revocation of the Edict of Nantes in 1685 (Louis XIV's effective elimination of Protestantism in France) resulted in a large number of emigrant Huguenot craftsmen settling in England. They brought with them many changes to English styles and techniques. A refinement of ornament was one of the most striking contributions of the Huguenots even when they were making wares in typically English form. Here Pierre Harache, the first of the refugee silversmiths to be admitted to the Freedom of the Goldsmiths' Company in 1698, gives the piercing of the caster top a delicacy and detail missing in the work of most English silversmiths. His treatment of the base, with its formal gadrooned border, reflects the ordered style of the Huguenots. It is interesting to note Mr A. G. Grimwade's comment that the work of Harache 'is of the highest standard of design and execution'.

LENT FROM THE COLLECTION OF THE WORSHIPFUL COMPANY OF GOLDSMITHS.

Gift in 1939 of R.R.J. Copeland, Prime Warden 1946.

Illustrated and described by Michael Clayton The Collectors' Dictionary *p.50 No.100.*

Plate XLV

A WILLIAM III oval Wine Cistern boldly embossed with ribs around the lower part on a matted ground with gadroon border, the lip chased with realistic palm leaves standing on a bold collet foot decorated with gadrooning. The handles surmounted by a demi-boar (the Warrington Supporter) emerging from 'S' scroll strapwork.

London, 1701/2
by Philip Rollos
Height, 15 inches
Width, 25 inches
Weight, 280 ounces

GEORGE (Booth) 2nd Earl of Warrington was born 2nd May 1675 at Mere Hall Chester and was 2nd but 1st surviving son of Henry (Booth) 1st Earl of Warrington created 1690; he succeeded to the title in 1694. He married 9th April 1702 at St. Giles–in–the–fields, Mary, daughter and co-heir of John Oldbury a London Merchant. A dowry reported to be £40,000 was settled upon the marriage which enabled George (Booth) 2nd Earl of Warrington to pay off his father's debts and delight in his passion for collecting silver, mainly by the Huguenot smiths, whose silver was of the highest quality and of a reasonable price. The fact that the Huguenots were Protestant would not have gone unnoticed.

His daughter Mary married Harry (Grey) Earl of Stamford who after her father's death lived at Dunham Massey with her husband. The Earls of Stamford continued to live at Dunham Massey until the home was passed as a gift to the National Trust in 1976.

LENT BY THE NATIONAL TRUST, DUNHAM MASSEY.

Foley Grey Sale, 1921
Further use of the Wine Cistern or Jardiniere can be observed in Interior Decoration in England, France and Holland *Peter Thornton, pl.304.*

Plate XLI,
The Warrington Supporters

Plate XLVII

A SCOTTISH toilet service of extremely plain outline, consisting of a large, plain, oblong casket with moulded borders and domed cover, engraved with a cypher surmounted by a Baron's coronet fitted with an internal metal sprung clasp. 10¾ inches long. The original lining with fabric covered wooden frame has not survived so the function of the box, whether for jewels or cosmetic items, cannot be determined.

Two pairs of plain circular boxes with pull-off lids similarly engraved, sizes 5⅜ inches and 3½ inches.

A pair of circular two-handled ecuelles and covers, also engraved. 5⅜ inches.

A pair of exquisite octagonal pounce pots of bombé form, the pull-off stoppers engraved with a cypher.

A pair of cast candlesticks each on a stepped octagonal base, with sunken centre, baluster stem and vase shaped socket, similar engraving. 5⅞ inches high.

A pair of plain oval brush backs with applied moulded band, similar engraving. 5⅝ inches long.

A pair of whisk handles af tapering octagonal outline and ball finial engraved with a coronet and cypher 4½ inches long.

A rectangular pin-cushion on four pad feet with moulded sides and engraved. 7 inches long.

An oblong mirror with moulded sides and reeded border with applied stylised oak leaves at the angles, fully hallmarked on each side. 19½ inches high.

THE CYPHER is that of the Honourable Marion Steward, eldest daughter of Alexander, 5th Lord Blantyre, who married James Sterling of Keir in 1704. It was common practice for the aristocracy and the wealthy to bestow upon the bride-to-be, a toilet service. Indeed it is certain that this fine Scottish toilet service was made for the marriage of the Honourable Marion Steward, and has remained in the family until its recent sale to the present owner.

James Sterling of Keir was born in 1679 and took part in the Stewart rising of 1715. Being a known sympathiser of the cause he was probably imprisoned during the rebellion of 1745. His marriage to the Honourable Marion Steward produced twenty-one children and he died in 1749.

The development of the toilet service began in the reign of Charles II, when ladies tastes seemed to demand more of their toilet utensils than was the case before the Civil War. The King and his
courtiers

Edinburgh, 1703/4 by Colin McKenzie Assay-master, James Penman

courtiers brought back from France a taste for lavishly embossed silver, and the relative wealth amongst the aristocracy and successful merchants encouraged silversmiths to be more adventurous and find new forms, among them, the toilet service.

John Evelyn, writing in 1690, still considered toilet services to be characteristically extravagant, although they had been in use for at least twenty years. In 'Mundus Muliebris' he wrote:

A new Scene to us next presents,
The Dressing Room and Implements,
Of Toilet Plate Gilt, and Emboss'd,
And several other things of cost,
The Table Miroir, one Glue Pot,
One for Pomatum and what-not?

Of Washes Unguents and Cosmeticks,
A pair of Silver Candlesticks,
Snuffers and Snuff-dish, Boxes more,
For Powders, Patches, Waters Store,
In Silver Flasks or Bottles, Cups,
Covered or open to wash chaps.

All these vessels are present in the Keir service.

PRIVATE LOAN.

Exhibited Scottish Art Academy *1939 No. 937.*
Collection of the Sterlings of Keir *1703–1982.*
Private Collection 1982.
Michael Clayton The Collectors' Dictionary of
Silver and Gold *London 1971. p.317.*
Charles Oman Caroline Silver *pp.62–3.*

J. Findlay Scottish Gold and Silver Work
London 1956. pp118–119. According to Findlay, this
is the only complete Scottish toilet set to have
survived. The candlesticks are cast from London
candlesticks of 1701 and traces of the London marks
are discernible in addition to those of Edinburgh.

Plate XLVIII

A PAIR of wall sconces each decorated with oak leaves surrounding a cherub's face. The C scroll arm protruding from the cherub's mouth supporting the escutcheon shaped guard holder, drip-pan and socket. The upper part of the back plate bears the coat of arms and supporters below a ducal coronet surmounted in turn by the crest, garter and coronet.

The coat of arms is of James, second son of the Duke of Queensbury, KG.

London, 1707/8
by David Williame
Height, 19¾ inches

THE arms are those of Douglas quartering Man and impaling Boyle for Man, fourth daughter of Charles Boyle Lord Clifford, whom the Duke married in 1685 and who died in 1711. The numbers N3 and N4 engraved on the reverse identify these as from a set split for sale; the later addition of a lamp-glass base to the drip-pan indicates their adaptation in the nineteenth century.

It is not uncommon for coats of arms to form an integral part of the design of the back plate.

The principle of lighting by means of fixed wall-mounted candle-holders was well established. Silver wall sconces were supplied for the royal palaces of Whitehall and Greenwich in the 1530s and their use in relatively modest interiors is demonstrated in Dutch and French engravings of the 1630s, but no example of an English silver sconce earlier than about 1660 has survived. Late 17th century sets exemplified the increased elaboration characteristic of the period and, as in this pair, the reflective quality of the plain burnished backplate was often sacrificed.

LENT BY THE VICTORIA AND ALBERT MUSEUM.

Formerly in the Brownlow Collection.
Purchased Christies *29th May, 1963.*
Thornton Seventeenth Century Interior Decoration in England, France and Holland *pl. 261.*

Michael Clayton The Collectors' Dictionary of Silver and Gold *No. 503.*

Plate XLIX

WINE Coolers of bombé shape, with nearly horizontal reeded handles, the lower part of the bodies is elaborately decorated with applied strapwork of lanceolate palm-leaves, shells and scrollwork. At a level with the handles is a broad band of strapwork and foliage with central shell cartouches each side. Thick applied lateral straps stretch the full height of the bodies, pass through the handles, and terminate as voluted masks which follow the everted shape of the necks. The flat outer rims are decorated with a husk pattern. The circular bases are chased with panels of diaper work divided alternately by small shell cartouches and strapwork.

London, circa 1720
by Philip Rollos
Engraved
with the Arms of
John, 1st Earl of Bristol,
[see No. 34]
Height, 10½ inches

MICHAEL Clayton remarks:
'About 1700 the need for a single bottle cooler was felt, probably at first on those rare occasions when the master of the great house was dining alone. John 1st Duke of Marlborough had an unmarked pair of solid gold (now in the British Museum). Also there is a superb pair by Philip Rollos at Ickworth, Suffolk.'

The date of acquisition is uncertain, however the majority of his purchases for the dining room were made between 1716 – 23. Although the Ickworth guide book suggests the date 1710 for these wine coolers, their engraved ornament, coupled with the likelihood that they were purchased by the Earl of Bristol as dining plate supports a later date.

LENT BY THE NATIONAL TRUST, ICKWORTH.

N.M. *Penzer* The Hervey Silver at Ickworth
Part I & II. *Apollo, 1957.*

M. *Clayton* The Collectors' Dictionary of Silver
& Gold *pl. 48 p. 339.*

Plate L

A SET of Casters of octagonal baluster form, the domed lid with circular baluster finial pierced and finely engraved, the body with sides of alternating width on stepped and moulded feet with gadroon decoration, the body engraved with a contemporary coat-of-arms.

London, 1723/4 by Paul de Lamerie. Height, 8½ inches and 6¼ inches.

THESE casters form part of a group of vinegar bottles and casters, all by the same maker in 1723, displayed at Ickworth. The Arms are those of Bristol impaling Felton for John Hervey 1st Earl of Bristol who married Elizabeth, daughter and heir of Sir Thomas Felton of Playford Hall, Suffolk. The Hervey family have owned the Ickworth estate since the middle of the fifteenth century. John Hervey, created Earl of Bristol in 1714 was the real founder of the family fortunes, marrying two heiresses and becoming a staunch Whig in the early years of the Glorious Revolution. The famous Duchess of Marlborough in her 'Conduct' wrote:

'I never was concerned in making any Peer but one, and that was my Lord Hervey, I had made a promise to Sir Thomas Felton that if her Majesty should ever make any new Lords I would certainly use my influence that Mr Hervey should be one. When the Queen had resolved to create four Peers, Granville, Guernsey, Gower and Conway, I wrote to Lord Marlborough and Lord Godolphin that if they did not endeavour to get Mr Hervey made a Peer I neither would, nor could, shew my face anymore. The thing was done purely at my request and at a time when affairs at Court ran so violently against the whole party of Whigs that Mr Hervey had laid aside all hopes of the Peerage'.

This peerage was one of fourteen created at the coronation on the 25th October 1714 of George I.

N. M. Penzer relates that these are graceful expressions of de Lamerie's conception of line in the true octagon, with four of the sides straight and the others alternate incurved.

It is amusing to record that for many years these two sets were regarded as mustard pots and used as such, the covers having long since been separated from the bodies. They were discovered some years ago in a box in the attic still in perfect condition.

LENT BY THE NATIONAL TRUST, ICKWORTH.

N. M. Penzer The Hervey Silver at Ickworth part II *Apollo, April 1957.*

Michael Clayton The Collector's Dictionary of Gold and Silver *plate 48 p.339.*

Plate LI

A GEORGE I rose-water ewer and dish, the helmet shaped ewer on circular foot with octagonal stem, chased with a border and panels of shells and strapwork, the lower part of the body with applied strapwork on matted ground and applied coat-of-arms above, with mask and shell below the lip and a shaped scroll moulding with rosettes at the sides, the boldly scrolling harp-shaped handle chased at the front with a bearded mask and on the back of the main member with guilloche ornament.

The circular dish with a cast and applied coat-of-arms in the centre in a baroque cartouche frame, the border with applied and chased medallion heads, masks, shells and strapwork, and the rim with panels of strapwork and foliage with leaf and scroll motifs at intervals.

London, 1726/7 by David Willaume Junior
Height of Ewer, 15 inches
Diameter of Dish, 25½ inches

THE arms are those of Watson-Wentworth impaling Finch for Thomas 1st Marquess of Rockingham, K.B., who married in 1716 Mary 4th daughter of Daniel 7th Earl of Winchelsea.

Compare the set made by de Lamerie *for* Sir George Treby *at the* Ashmolean Museum, *also of the* mid-1720s.

Plate LII

FOUNTAIN of unusual size chased with male and female masks within an applied cartouche, bands of shells, palm leaves and strapwork; the ribs and vertical palm leaves around the lower parts; the handles designed as demi-boars (the Warrington Supporters) and the cover similarly decorated surmounted by an Earl's Coronet. Engraved inside foot. This fountain was made for George Booth, 2nd Earl of Warrington in 1728 by Peter Archambo.'

London, 1728/9
by Peter Archambo
Height, 25 inches

IT is interesting to note that this object was sold in the Foley-Grey sale Lot 121 for £287.10 to Parsons and described as a George II Tea-urn, see *No. 19.*

Originally made to order for the famed patron of his time, George Booth, second Earl of Warrington – the rampant boars are part of the family coat-of-arms. Wine fountains and their frequent counterparts, wine cisterns, are amongst the greatest largest wrought silver objects ever made, reflecting the great social status attached to these, and also the immense appetite for food and wine of 18th Century Englishmen. Weighing 557 ounces, it survived as a duty dodger until re-assayed and re-marked in 1929. Archambo had evaded the plate duty charge of 6d per ounce, saving himself £14 18s 6d. which the 1719 act required to be collected by the Assay office, by only sending a small salver which he subsequently had let into the bottom of the fountain. He was never a member of the Goldsmiths Company.

FROM THE COLLECTION OF THE WORSHIPFUL COMPANY OF GOLDSMITHS.

Foley-Grey Sale, 1921.
The gift, in 1945, of L.W.B. Parsons and
H.M. Parsons *the latter* Prime Warden, *1948.*

John F. Hayward Huguenot Silver in England,
1688–1727 *pp.37–38.*
The Catalogue Touching Gold and Silver
Exhibition *Goldsmiths Hall, 1978 Nov. 86 & 87.*

Plate LIII

THE Walpole Salver square on four scroll feet, the central roundel is engraved with both faces of the last Exchequer Seal of George I, supported by Hercules with Calumny and Envy in chains at his feet before a distant panorama of London. Above, two virtues in clouds complete the composition. Around the edge of the salver is an elaborately engraved border broken by corner medallions containing the arms of Sir Robert Walpole (1671–1745) quartered with those of his wife Catherine Shorter, his crest and cypher.

London, 1728/9 by Paul de Lamerie Engraving attributed to William Hogarth. Size, 19½ inches, square

ALTHOUGH the engraving on this, the finest of the series of late Stuart and Georgian seal salvers, was attributed to Hogarth as early as 1781, his authorship has been disputed more recently. The design of the two matrices themselves could not of course be adapted by the engraver but he has incorporated such additional elements as a view of London and the skilfully rendered allegorical group; Envy first appeared on the Great Seal of George I in reference to the Earl of Mar's rebellion in 1715. Charles Oman strongly reasserted Hogarth's responsibility for the engraving of this salver. The similarity of the complex border, with its trellis panels interrupted by masks in shell-tipped frames, to other work by Lamerie (a basin of 1722 in the Ashmolean and around the cistern of 1726 in the Hermitage) indicate that this pattern was regularly in use in his workshop for decorating higher quality commissions, and this might be an argument against the attribution of the whole to Hogarth, since no-one has suggested that he was regularly employed to work on silver after his apprenticeship.

It is not known why Walpole should have been the fortunate recipient of two Exchequer seals; this was the seal in use at the Exchequer between 1724 and the death of George I in 1727. The custom whereby the silver seal matrix became a perquisite of the officeholder once it was redundant, had originated in the 15th century. Since the matrix weighed about 120 ounces, the recipient was enabled to make a substantial commemorative piece or, as in the case of Sir Nicholas Bacon, a cup for each of his three sons.

LENT BY THE VICTORIA AND ALBERT MUSEUM.

Strawberry Hill Sale *6th May 1842, Lot 120*
Charles Oman English Engraved Silver *pp.59–60*
Judith Bannister Silver Seal Cups and Salvers
Country Life, 29th January and 5th February 1981.

Philip A.S. Phillips Paul de Lamerie *pl.LX LXI pp.86–90.*

Plate LIV The slight streaking is the result of lacquering.

A PAIR of silver-gilt bowls and covers with plain shaped sides standing on circular collet feet, the covers conical shaped engraved, one with the coat-of-arms of George Booth, 2nd Earl of Warrington, the other with his cypher.

London, 1730/31
by Peter Archambo
Height, 6 inches

THESE containers are of the shape and size normally found in toilet services. Archambo was supplying large quantities of plate to Booth at this time but the great bulk of his production was dining room plate such as the massive cistern of 1729, the breadbasket (1730) and salvers, a pair of covered cups and six sconces, all still at Dunham Massey. However, in 1728 Isaac Liger supplied parts of a toilet service; it is possible that these were purchased to make the service more comprehensive. It is noteworthy that these are gilt, much of the Booth plate is silver-gilt.

LENT BY THE NATIONAL TRUST, DUNHAM MASSEY.

Foley-Grey sale 1921.

Plate LV

HER MAJESTY QUEEN ELIZABETH II

THE VICTORIA AND ALBERT MUSEUM
Brompton Road, London SW7.

THE NATIONAL TRUST
42 Queen Anne's Gate, London SW1.

HAMPSHIRE COUNTY MUSEUM SERVICE
for the Deane Cup, which resides at the Willis Museum,
New Street, Basingstoke, Hampshire.

SOUTHAMPTON MUSEUM SERVICE
for lending the St. Michael's Cup which is on display at
Tudor House Museum, St. Michael's Square, Southampton.

ALL OUR VERY GENEROUS PRIVATE COLLECTORS.

BRAND INGLIS, ESQ.
for his invaluable information on the Elizabeth I Cup 1598.

PETER WALDRON ESQ.
Sotheby's, 34–35 New Bond Street, London W1.

TIM SCHROUDER ESQ.
Christies, King Street, London W1.

SETTRINGTON & BOOTES-JOHNS,
Design Consultants, 245 New Kings Road, London SW6.

J. F. D. CHARLES, APRIL 1983

Reverend P.R.P. Braithwaite, Church Plate of Hampshire, *London 1909.*

Cambridge Plate, The Fitzwilliam Museum, 1975.

Catalogue, Loan Exhibition, 25 Park Lane, 1929.

Christies Silver Treasures from English Churches, *1955.*

Michael Clayton, The Collectors' Dictionary of Silver and Gold, *London 1971.*

J.K.D. Cooper, A re-assessment of some English Late Gothic and Early Renaissance Plate. *Burlington Magazine, Volume CXI, 1978.*

T.S. Cooper, Church Plate of Surrey, *London 1902.*

Country Life, Church Treasures in Peril, *February 7th, 1974.*

J. Findlay, Scottish Gold and Silver Work, *London 1956.*

Fredericks, Dutch Silver, *Volume II.*

Freshfield, The Communion Plate...The County of London, *London 1895.*

Goldsmiths Hall, Touching Gold and Silver Exhibition, *1978.*

Goldsmiths Hall, Exhibition of the Historic Plate of the City of London at Goldsmiths Hall, 1951.

A. G. Grimwade, London Goldsmiths 1697–1837, *Second Edition, London 1982.*

E. Hackenbroch, English and Other Silver in the Irwin Untermyer Collection, *revised 1969.*

J.F. Hayward, Virtuoso Goldsmiths and the Triumph of Mannerism, *1540–1620, London 1976.*

J.F. Hayward, Huguenot Silver in England, 1688–1727, *London 1959.*

Hind, History of Engraving in England, *volume II.*

Jewitt and Hope, Corporation Plate and Insignia of Office, *London 1895.*

Sir Charles Jackson, A History of English Plate, *Volumes I and II, 1911.*

Roger Lushington, The Tankards of Sir Edmund Bury Godfrey,
Connoisseur CXC, 1975.

Charles Oman, Caroline Silver 1625–1688, *London 1970.*

Charles Oman, English Silversmiths Work, Civil and Domestic,
HMSO, 1965.

Charles Oman, English Engraved Silver, 1150–1900, *London, 1978.*

Charles Oman, The English Silver in the Kremlin, 1557–1663, *London 1961.*

Charles Oman and Jonathan Mayne, Six Elizabethan Gilt Plates,
Burlington Magazine, 1946, Volume 88.

N.M. Penzer, Tudor Font Shaped Cups, *Apollo, November 1957,
February/March 1958.*

N.M. Penzer, The Hervey Silver at Ickworth, *Apollo, February and April,
parts I and II, 1957.*

N.M. Penzer, An index of Steeple Cups, Society of Silver Collectors,
special paper 1962.

J. Starkie Gardner F.S.A., Old Silver Work From 15th to
18th Centuries, *Loan Collection 1902.*

Surtees Society, Diary of Sir Walter Calverley, *1886.* Yorkshire Diaries and
Biographies of the 17th and 18th Centuries.

Peter Thornton, Seventeenth-century Interior Decoration in England, France
and Holland, *Newhaven and London, 1978.*